Contents

The following sample exam paper is a printed representation of how this exam will appear when online. The structure of the questions, the knowledge required and the topics covered will be the same. However, in order to suit an online platform, the wording of the questions and the method of answering them may be different.

Terminology:

bar	semibreve	minim	crotchet	quaver	semiquaver
measure	whole note	half note	quarter note	8th note	16th note

Music Theory Sample Paper 2020 Grade 1 A

Exam duration: 1½ hours maximum

1 Rhythm

/15

1.1 Circle the correct time signature for each of these bars.

(3)

(a) $\qquad$ **C** $\frac{3}{4}$ $\frac{2}{4}$

(b) $\qquad$ $\frac{4}{4}$ $\frac{2}{4}$ $\frac{3}{4}$

(c) $\qquad$ $\frac{2}{4}$ $\frac{3}{4}$ $\frac{4}{4}$

1.2 Add the **one** missing bar-line to **each** of these five melodies.

(5)

(a)

(b)

(c)

(d)

(e)

1.3 Tick (✔) **one** box to answer each question.

(2)

(a) How many ♩ are there in a semibreve?   2 ☐   4 ☐   6 ☐   8 ☐

(b) How many quavers are there in a minim?   2 ☐   3 ☐   4 ☐   6 ☐

1.4 Tick (✔) **one** box to show which bar is grouped correctly.

(1)

☐   ☐   ☐

Music Theory
Sample Papers

for new format Theory exams

ABRSM Grade 1

Music Theory Sample Papers

These sample papers have been created to prepare candidates for our new format theory exams from 2020.

What's new for Grade 1?

- There are new question types including more multiple-choice. This is to ensure objective, reliable and robust assessment.
- Candidates are now no longer required to demonstrate accurate copying of music however the knowledge they will be required to show in their answers will be the same.
- There will be a total of 75 marks available rather than 100 marks. Candidates will need 50 marks for a Pass, 60 marks for a Merit and 65 marks for a Distinction.

What's changing for Grade 1?

- A reduced number of terms and signs, which now better supports progression from grade to grade and ensures the required knowledge is more relevant and useful to learners.

New supporting publications

Discovering Music Theory

Discovering Music Theory is a suite of workbooks and corresponding answer books that offers all-round preparation for the updated ABRSM Music Theory exams from 2020, including the new online papers. These full-colour workbooks will equip students of all ages with the skills, knowledge and understanding required for the ABRSM Grades 1–5 Music Theory exams. Written to make theory engaging and relevant to developing musicians of all ages.

© 2020 by The Associated Board of the Royal Schools of Music
Published by ABRSM (Publishing) Ltd, a wholly owned subsidiary of ABRSM
Cover by Andy Potts
Printed in England by Halstan & Co. Ltd, Amersham, Bucks, on materials from sustainable sources
P14799

1.5 Tick (✔) or cross (✗) **each** box to show whether the rests are correct **or** incorrect. (3)

1.6 Tick (✔) **one** box which shows the four notes written in order from the **longest** value to the **shortest**. (1)

2 Pitch /15

2.1 Tick (✔) **one** box to show the correct name of each note. (7)

(a) F F♯ D B

(b) E B A G

(c) C B A E

(d) B♭ E♭ G♭ A♭

(e) F A C B

(f) F♯ C♯ D♯ G♯

(g) E C F B♭

2.2 Tick (✔) the **lower** note of each of the pairs of notes. (4)

(a) (b) (c) (d)

2.3 Tick (✔) the correct clef needed to make each of these named notes. (4)

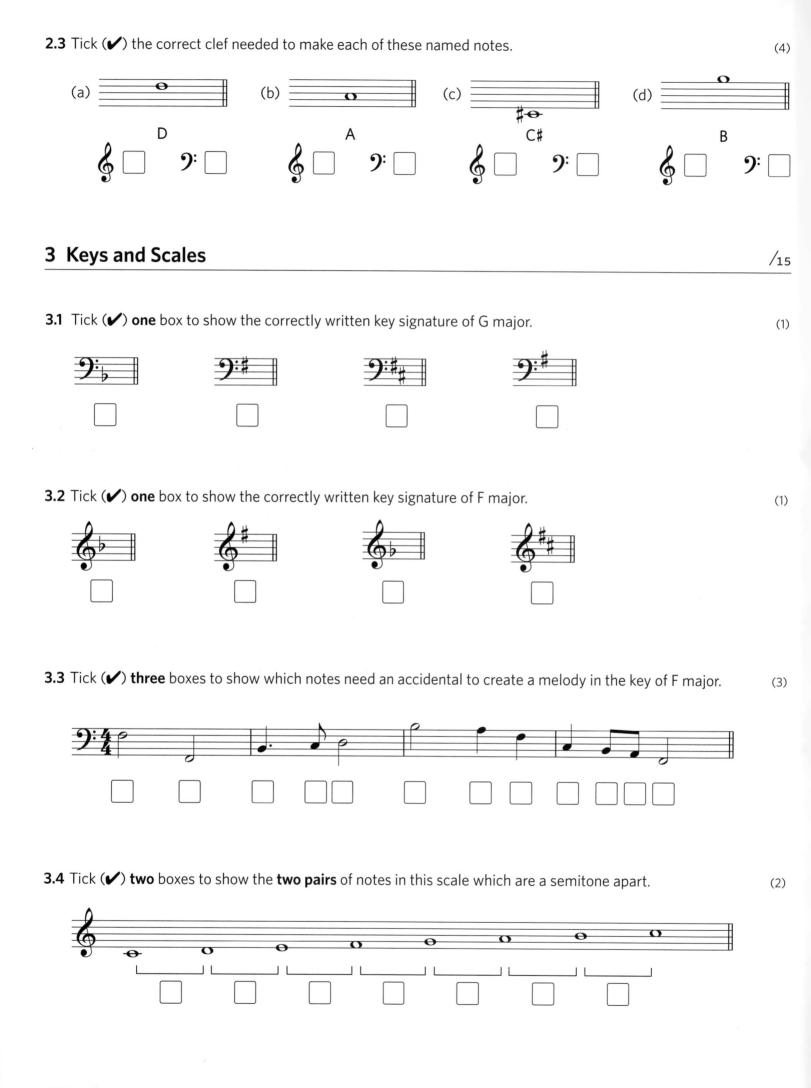

3 Keys and Scales

/15

3.1 Tick (✔) **one** box to show the correctly written key signature of G major. (1)

3.2 Tick (✔) **one** box to show the correctly written key signature of F major. (1)

3.3 Tick (✔) **three** boxes to show which notes need an accidental to create a melody in the key of F major. (3)

3.4 Tick (✔) **two** boxes to show the **two pairs** of notes in this scale which are a semitone apart. (2)

3.5 Circle **TRUE** or **FALSE** for each statement. (4)

(a) There are two sharps in the key signature of D major   **TRUE**   **FALSE**

(b) There is an F sharp in the key signature of G major   **TRUE**   **FALSE**

(c) 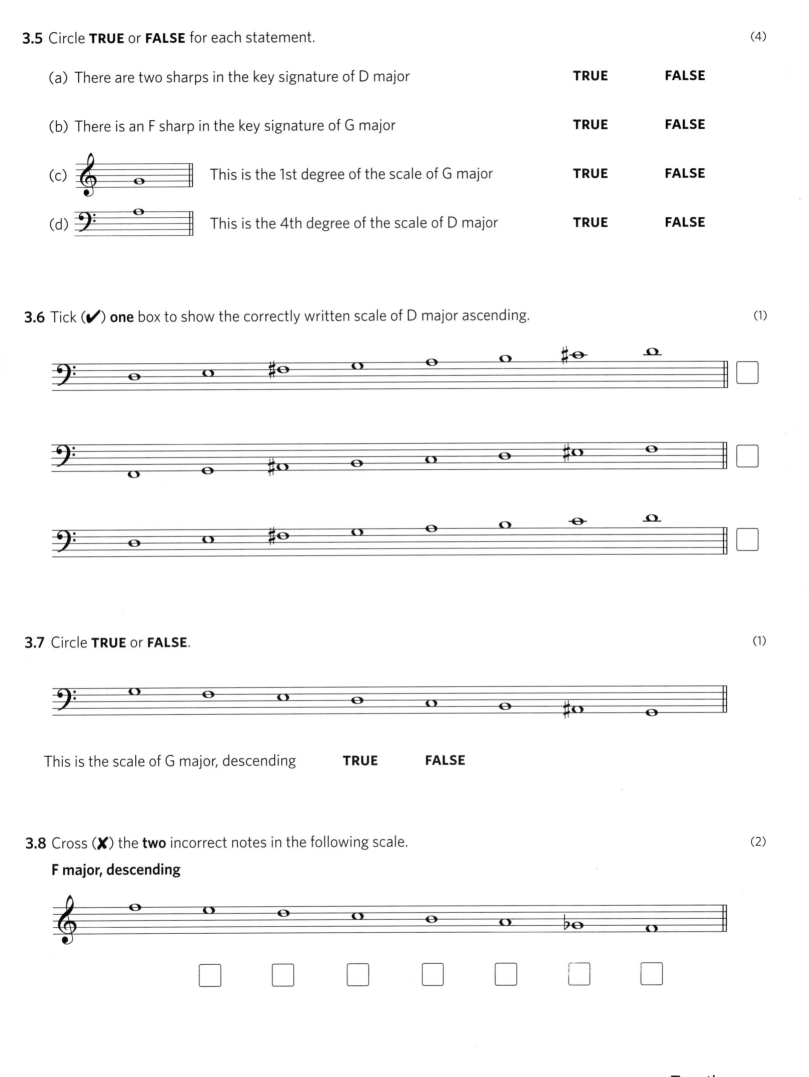 This is the 1st degree of the scale of G major   **TRUE**   **FALSE**

(d) This is the 4th degree of the scale of D major   **TRUE**   **FALSE**

3.6 Tick (✔) **one** box to show the correctly written scale of D major ascending. (1)

3.7 Circle **TRUE** or **FALSE**. (1)

This is the scale of G major, descending   **TRUE**   **FALSE**

3.8 Cross (✘) the **two** incorrect notes in the following scale. (2)

F major, descending

4 Intervals

4.1 For each example, write one note to form the named interval.
Your note should be **higher** than the given note. The key is F major.

(5)

(a)

5th

(b)

8th / 8ve

(c)

2nd

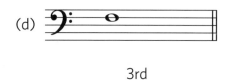

(d)

3rd

(e)

7th

4.2 Tick (✔) **one** box to show the correct number of each interval. The key is G major.

(5)

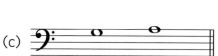

(a)

5th	6th	7th	8th/8ve
☐	☐	☐	☐

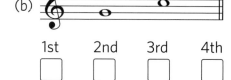

(b)

1st	2nd	3rd	4th
☐	☐	☐	☐

(c)

2nd	3rd	4th	5th
☐	☐	☐	☐

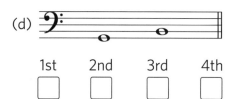

(d)

1st	2nd	3rd	4th
☐	☐	☐	☐

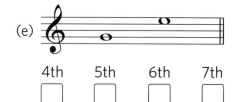

(e)

4th	5th	6th	7th
☐	☐	☐	☐

5 Tonic Triads

5.1 Circle **TRUE** or **FALSE** for each statement.

(3)

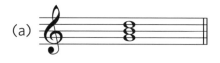

(a)   This is the tonic triad of G major   **TRUE**   **FALSE**

(b)   This is the tonic triad of F major   **TRUE**   **FALSE**

(c)   This is the tonic triad of C major   **TRUE**   **FALSE**

5.2 Add **one** missing note to complete each triad, with the tonic as the lowest note. (3)
Use accidentals if necessary.

(a)

D major

(b)

C major

(c)

G major

5.3 Circle the correct key for each tonic triad. (4)

(a)   C major   G major   D major   F major

(b)   G major   C major   F major   D major

(c)   F major   C major   G major   D major

(d)   D major   G major   C major   F major

6 Terms and Signs   /5

Tick (✔) **one** box for each term/sign. (5)

means:

slur: detached ☐

tie: detached ☐

tie: hold the value of both notes ☐

slur: perform smoothly ☐

♩ = 60 means:

60 crotchet notes ☐

60 crotchet beats ☐

60 crotchet beats in a minute ☐

60 crotchet beats in a bar ☐

ritardando means:

gradually getting slower ☐

gradually getting quicker ☐

gradually getting louder ☐

gradually getting quieter ☐

dolce means:

sweet ☐

smoothly ☐

slow ☐

in a singing style ☐

p means:

moderately quiet ☐

quiet ☐

very quiet ☐

very loud ☐

Look at this melody and then answer the questions that follow.

7.1 Circle **TRUE** or **FALSE**.

(1)

The melody gets gradually slower towards the end   **TRUE**   **FALSE**

7.2 Tick (✔) the bar number that contains all the notes of the tonic triad of G major.

(1)

bar 3 ☐   bar 5 ☐   bar 6 ☐   bar 7 ☐

7.3 Complete the following **three** sentences by ticking one box for each.

(3)

(a) The **shortest** note in the melody is a …

crotchet ☐   semiquaver ☐   quaver ☐   minim ☐

(b) Bar 2 has the same rhythm as …

bar 3 ☐   bar 5 ☐   bar 6 ☐   bar 7 ☐

(c) The letter name of the **lowest** note in the melody is …

E ☐   F♯ ☐   G ☐   C ☐

Music Theory Sample Paper 2020 Grade 1 B

Exam duration: 1½ hours maximum

Total marks: /75

1 Rhythm

/15

1.1 Circle the correct time signature for each of these bars. (3)

(a)

$\frac{2}{4}$ $\frac{3}{4}$ C

(b)

$\frac{4}{4}$ $\frac{3}{4}$ $\frac{2}{4}$

(c)

$\frac{3}{4}$ C $\frac{2}{4}$

1.2 Add the **one** missing bar-line to **each** of these five melodies. (5)

(a)

(b)

(c)

(d)

(e)

1.3 Tick (✔) **one** box to answer each question. (2)

(a) How many semiquavers are there in a minim?   2 ☐   4 ☐   6 ☐   8 ☐

(b) How many ♩ are there in a semibreve?   2 ☐   3 ☐   4 ☐   6 ☐

1.4 Tick (✔) **one** box to show which bar is grouped correctly. (1)

☐

☐

☐

Turn the page

1.5 Tick (✔) or cross (✘) **each** box to show whether the rests are correct **or** incorrect. (3)

1.6 Tick (✔) **one** box which shows the four notes written in order from the **shortest** value to the **longest**. (1)

2 Pitch

/15

2.1 Tick (✔) **one** box to show the correct name of each note. (7)

(a) G F B D

(b) G B♭ E D

(c) B♭ G♭ E♭ A♭

(d) D B C F

(e) A F B C

(f) G♯ C♯ F♯ D♯

(g) F♯ C♯ C E

2.2 Tick (✔) the **higher** note of each of the pairs of notes. (4)

(a) (b) (c) (d)

2.3 Tick (✔) the correct clef needed to make each of these named notes. (4)

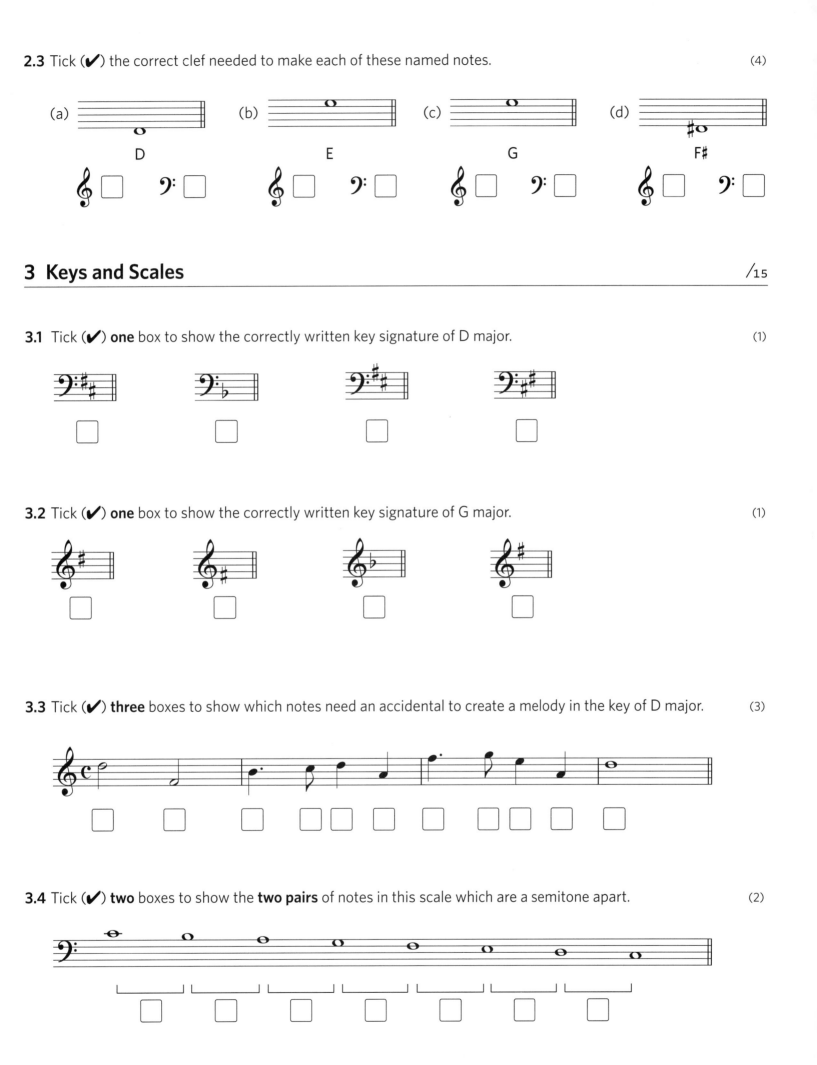

3 Keys and Scales /15

3.1 Tick (✔) **one** box to show the correctly written key signature of D major. (1)

3.2 Tick (✔) **one** box to show the correctly written key signature of G major. (1)

3.3 Tick (✔) **three** boxes to show which notes need an accidental to create a melody in the key of D major. (3)

3.4 Tick (✔) **two** boxes to show the **two pairs** of notes in this scale which are a semitone apart. (2)

Turn the page

3.5 Circle **TRUE** or **FALSE** for each statement. (4)

(a) There are no sharps or flats in the key signature of C major   **TRUE**   **FALSE**

(b) There is an F sharp in the key signature of G major   **TRUE**   **FALSE**

(c) 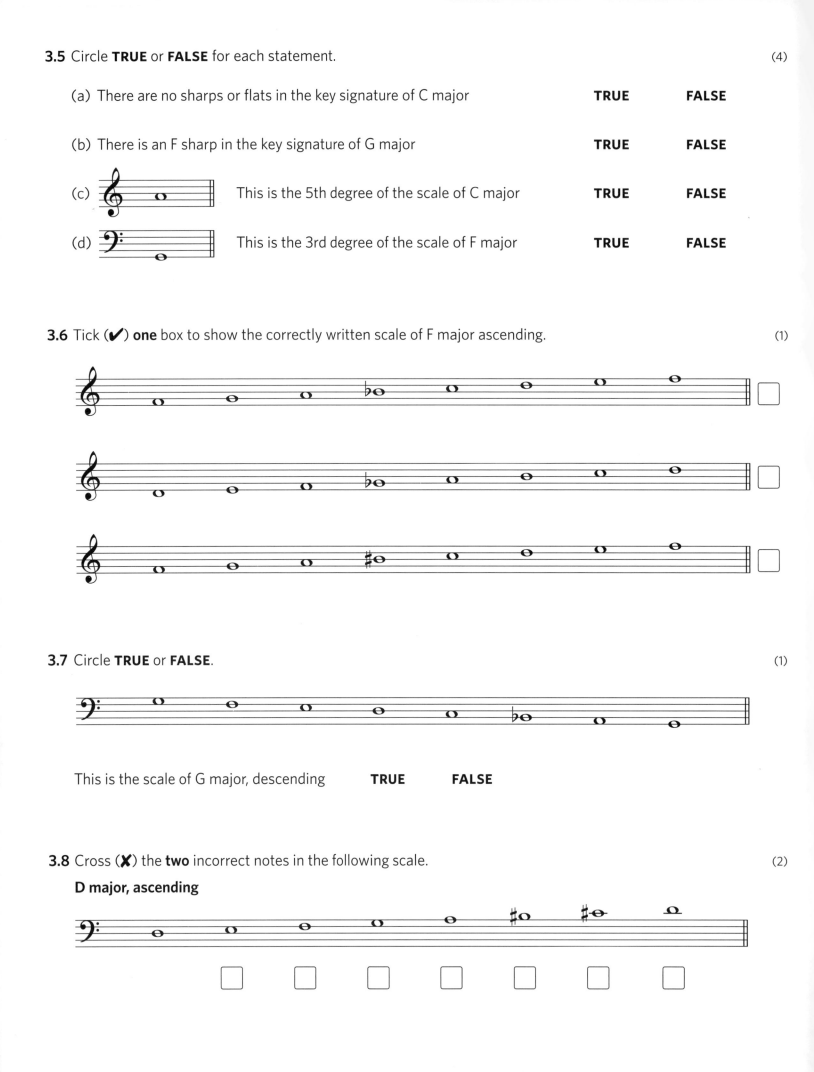 This is the 5th degree of the scale of C major   **TRUE**   **FALSE**

(d) This is the 3rd degree of the scale of F major   **TRUE**   **FALSE**

3.6 Tick (✔) **one** box to show the correctly written scale of F major ascending. (1)

3.7 Circle **TRUE** or **FALSE**. (1)

This is the scale of G major, descending   **TRUE**   **FALSE**

3.8 Cross (✗) the **two** incorrect notes in the following scale. (2)

D major, ascending

4 Intervals

4.1 For each example, write one note to form the named interval.
Your note should be **higher** than the given note. The key is D major. (5)

(a) 6th

(b) 2nd

(c) 4th

(d) 8th / 8ve

(e) 5th

4.2 Tick (✔) **one** box to show the correct number of each interval. The key is F major. (5)

(a)
5th	6th	7th	8th/8ve
☐	☐	☐	☐

(b)
1st	2nd	3rd	4th
☐	☐	☐	☐

(c)
2nd	3rd	4th	5th
☐	☐	☐	☐

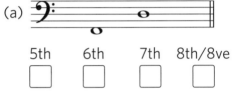

(d)
4th	5th	6th	7th
☐	☐	☐	☐

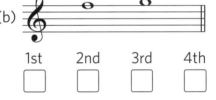

(e)
5th	6th	7th	8th/8ve
☐	☐	☐	☐

5 Tonic Triads

5.1 Circle **TRUE** or **FALSE** for each statement. (3)

(a) This is the tonic triad of G major   **TRUE**   **FALSE**

(b) This is the tonic triad of F major   **TRUE**   **FALSE**

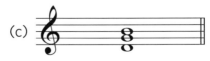

(c) This is the tonic triad of D major   **TRUE**   **FALSE**

5.2 Add **one** missing note to complete each triad, with the tonic as the lowest note. (3)
Use accidentals if necessary.

(a) [treble clef triad] G major

(b) [treble clef triad] C major

(c) [bass clef triad] D major

5.3 Circle the correct key for each tonic triad. (4)

(a) [treble clef triad]   C major   D major   F major   G major

(b) [treble clef triad]   C major   F major   G major   D major

(c) [bass clef triad]   G major   F major   D major   C major

(d) [bass clef triad]   D major   C major   G major   F major

6 Terms and Signs   /5

Tick (✔) **one** box for each term/sign. (5)

a tempo means:

in time	☐
the end	☐
slow	☐
gradually getting quicker	☐

cantabile means:

repeat from the beginning	☐
in a singing style	☐
at a medium speed	☐
smoothly	☐

⟨hairpin⟩ means:

gradually getting louder	☐
gradually getting quieter	☐
gradually getting slower	☐
gradually getting quicker	☐

mf means:

quiet	☐
moderately quiet	☐
very loud	☐
moderately loud	☐

[accent/staccato note] means:

staccato: detached	☐
staccato: smoothly	☐
accent the note	☐
legato: detached	☐

Look at this melody and then answer the questions that follow.

7.1 Circle **TRUE** or **FALSE**.   (1)

The melody gets gradually quieter towards the end   **TRUE**   **FALSE**

7.2 Tick (✔) the bar number that contains all the notes of the tonic triad of F major.   (1)

bar 1 ☐   bar 2 ☐   bar 3 ☐   bar 7 ☐

7.3 Complete the following **three** sentences by ticking one box for each.   (3)

(a) The **longest** note in the melody is a …

dotted crotchet ☐   semiquaver ☐   crotchet ☐   minim ☐

(b) Bar 2 has the same pitches as …

bar 1 ☐   bar 4 ☐   bar 5 ☐   bar 6 ☐

(c) The letter name of the **lowest** note in the melody is …

D ☐   F ☐   B♭ ☐   G ☐

Music Theory Sample Paper 2020 Grade 1 C

Exam duration: 1½ hours maximum

Total marks: ___ /75

1 Rhythm

/15

1.1 Circle the correct time signature for each of these bars. (3)

(a)  $\frac{2}{4}$ $\frac{3}{4}$ C

(b)  $\frac{4}{4}$ $\frac{2}{4}$ $\frac{3}{4}$

(c)  C $\frac{2}{4}$ $\frac{3}{4}$

1.2 Add the **one** missing bar-line to **each** of these five melodies. (5)

(a)

(b)

(c)

(d)

(e)

1.3 Tick (✔) **one** box to answer each question. (2)

(a) How many minims are there in a semibreve?   2 ☐   4 ☐   5 ☐   6 ☐

(b) How many ♪ are there in a crotchet?   2 ☐   3 ☐   4 ☐   8 ☐

1.4 Tick (✔) **one** box to show which bar is grouped correctly. (1)

☐   ☐   ☐

1.5 Tick (✔) or cross (✘) **each** box to show whether the rests are correct **or** incorrect. (3)

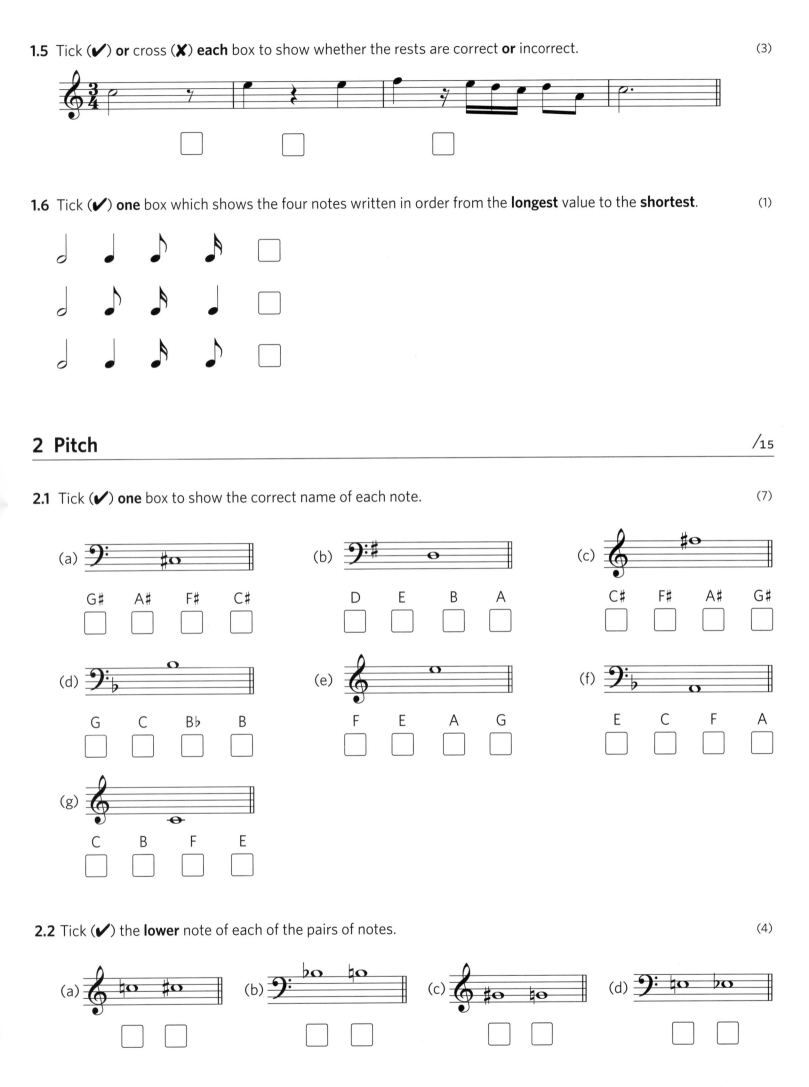

1.6 Tick (✔) **one** box which shows the four notes written in order from the **longest** value to the **shortest**. (1)

2 Pitch

/15

2.1 Tick (✔) **one** box to show the correct name of each note. (7)

(a)

G♯ A♯ F♯ C♯

(b)

D E B A

(c)

C♯ F♯ A♯ G♯

(d)

G C B♭ B

(e)

F E A G

(f)

E C F A

(g)

C B F E

2.2 Tick (✔) the **lower** note of each of the pairs of notes. (4)

(a) (b) (c) (d)

2.3 Tick (✔) the correct clef needed to make each of these named notes. (4)

3 Keys and Scales /15

3.1 Tick (✔) **one** box to show the correctly written key signature of G major. (1)

3.2 Tick (✔) **one** box to show the correctly written key signature of D major. (1)

3.3 Tick (✔) **three** boxes to show which notes need an accidental to create a melody in the key of F major. (3)

3.4 Tick (✔) **two** boxes to show the **two pairs** of notes in this scale which are a semitone apart. (2)

3.5 Circle **TRUE** or **FALSE** for each statement. (4)

(a) There are two sharps in the key signature of G major — **TRUE** **FALSE**

(b) There no sharps or flats in the key signature of C major — **TRUE** **FALSE**

(c) 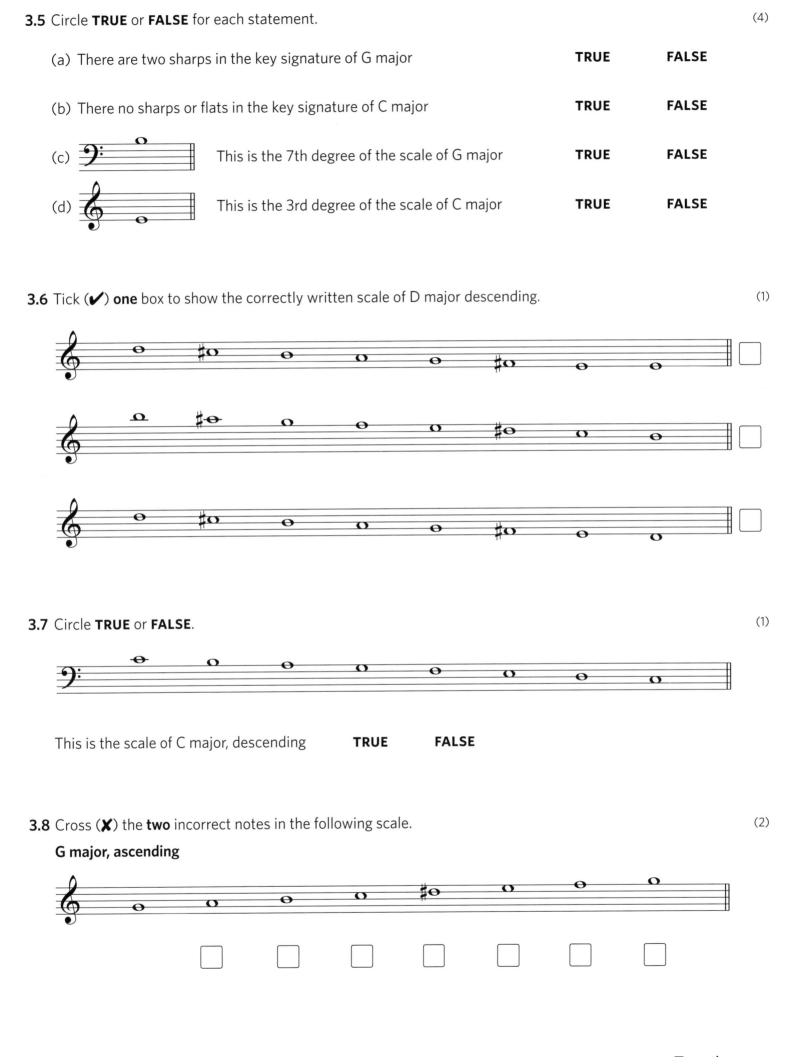 This is the 7th degree of the scale of G major — **TRUE** **FALSE**

(d) This is the 3rd degree of the scale of C major — **TRUE** **FALSE**

3.6 Tick (✔) **one** box to show the correctly written scale of D major descending. (1)

3.7 Circle **TRUE** or **FALSE**. (1)

This is the scale of C major, descending — **TRUE** **FALSE**

3.8 Cross (✗) the **two** incorrect notes in the following scale. (2)

G major, ascending

4 Intervals

4.1 For each example, write one note to form the named interval.
Your note should be **higher** than the given note. The key is G major.

(5)

2nd

4th

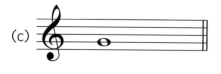

8th / 8ve

3rd

5th

4.2 Tick (✔) **one** box to show the correct number of each interval. The key is C major.

(5)

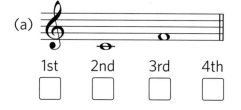

1st	2nd	3rd	4th
☐	☐	☐	☐

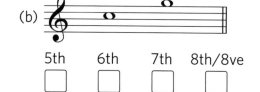

5th	6th	7th	8th/8ve
☐	☐	☐	☐

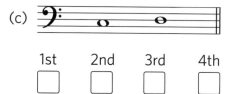

1st	2nd	3rd	4th
☐	☐	☐	☐

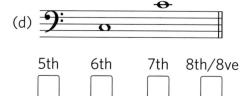

5th	6th	7th	8th/8ve
☐	☐	☐	☐

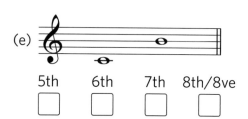

5th	6th	7th	8th/8ve
☐	☐	☐	☐

5 Tonic Triads

5.1 Circle **TRUE** or **FALSE** for each statement.

(3)

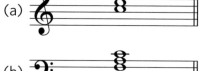 This is the tonic triad of C major   **TRUE**   **FALSE**

 This is the tonic triad of F major   **TRUE**   **FALSE**

 This is the tonic triad of D major   **TRUE**   **FALSE**

5.2 Add **one** missing note to complete each triad, with the tonic as the lowest note. (3)
Use accidentals if necessary.

(a) C major

(b) G major

(c) F major

5.3 Circle the correct key for each tonic triad. (4)

(a) C major   D major   F major   G major

(b) F major   C major   D major   G major

(c) C major   G major   D major   F major

(d) G major   F major   C major   D major

6 Terms and Signs /5

Tick (✔) **one** box for each term/sign. (5)

f means:

moderately quiet ☐
loud ☐
very loud ☐
moderately loud ☐

rallentando means:

gradually getting slower ☐
gradually getting quicker ☐
gradually getting louder ☐
slow ☐

⎯⎯⎯⎯ means:

gradually getting louder ☐
gradually getting quieter ☐
accent the note ☐
quiet ☐

legato means:

slow ☐
very quiet ☐
detached ☐
smoothly ☐

D.C. (da capo) means:

repeat from the beginning ☐
in a singing style ☐
the end ☐
in time ☐

Look at this melody and then answer the questions that follow.

7.1 Circle **TRUE** or **FALSE**.

(1)

The melody gets gradually louder towards the end   **TRUE**   **FALSE**

7.2 Tick (✔) the bar number that contains all the notes of the tonic triad of C major.

(1)

bar 3 ☐   bar 4 ☐   bar 5 ☐   bar 6 ☐

7.3 Complete the following **three** sentences by ticking one box for each.

(3)

(a) The **longest** note in the melody is a …

minim ☐   crotchet ☐   quaver ☐   dotted minim ☐

(b) Bar 5 has the same rhythm as …

bar 1 ☐   bar 2 ☐   bar 4 ☐   bar 6 ☐

(c) The letter name of the **lowest** note in the melody is …

D ☐   G ☐   E ☐   F♯ ☐

Music Theory Sample Paper 2020 Grade 1 D

Exam duration: 1½ hours maximum

Total marks: /75

1 Rhythm

/15

1.1 Circle the correct time signature for each of these bars. (3)

(a)  $\frac{4}{4}$ $\frac{2}{4}$ $\frac{3}{4}$

(b)  $\frac{2}{4}$ $\frac{4}{4}$ $\frac{3}{4}$

(c)  $\frac{3}{4}$ **C** $\frac{2}{4}$

1.2 Add the **one** missing bar-line to **each** of these five melodies. (5)

(a)

(b)

(c)

(d)

(e)

1.3 Tick (✔) **one** box to answer each question. (2)

(a) How many crotchets are there in a 𝅗𝅥. ?   3 ☐   4 ☐   5 ☐   7 ☐

(b) How many quavers are there in a crotchet?   2 ☐   4 ☐   6 ☐   8 ☐

1.4 Tick (✔) **one** box to show which bar is grouped correctly. (1)

☐   ☐   ☐

Turn the page

1.5 Tick (✔) or cross (✘) **each** box to show whether the rests are correct **or** incorrect. (3)

1.6 Tick (✔) **one** box which shows the four notes written in order from the **shortest** value to the **longest**. (1)

2 Pitch

/15

2.1 Tick (✔) **one** box to show the correct name of each note. (7)

(a)

C♯	B	C	E
☐	☐	☐	☐

(b)

A	E	F	G
☐	☐	☐	☐

(c)

D	F	E	G
☐	☐	☐	☐

(d)

E♭	G♭	B♭	A♭
☐	☐	☐	☐

(e)

D♯	F♯	C♯	G♯
☐	☐	☐	☐

(f)

A	G	B	D
☐	☐	☐	☐

(g)

E	D	G	B
☐	☐	☐	☐

2.2 Tick (✔) the **higher** note of each of the pairs of notes. (4)

2.3 Tick (✔) the correct clef needed to make each of these named notes. (4)

(a)

C#

𝄞 ☐ 𝄢 ☐

(b)

F

𝄞 ☐ 𝄢 ☐

(c)

A

𝄞 ☐ 𝄢 ☐

(d)

E

𝄞 ☐ 𝄢 ☐

3 Keys and Scales   /15

3.1 Tick (✔) **one** box to show the correctly written key signature of D major. (1)

☐   ☐   ☐   ☐

3.2 Tick (✔) **one** box to show the correctly written key signature of G major. (1)

☐   ☐   ☐   ☐

3.3 Tick (✔) **three** boxes to show which notes need an accidental to create a melody in the key of D major. (3)

☐ ☐ ☐ ☐ ☐ ☐☐ ☐☐ ☐ ☐ ☐

3.4 Tick (✔) **two** boxes to show the **two pairs** of notes in this scale which are a semitone apart. (2)

☐   ☐   ☐   ☐   ☐   ☐   ☐

3.5 Circle **TRUE** or **FALSE** for each statement. (4)

(a) There is one flat in the key signature of G major   **TRUE**   **FALSE**

(b) There is an F sharp in the key signature of C major   **TRUE**   **FALSE**

(c) This is the 5th degree of the scale of G major   **TRUE**   **FALSE**

(d) This is the 1st degree of the scale of C major   **TRUE**   **FALSE**

3.6 Tick (✔) **one** box to show the correctly written scale of G major ascending. (1)

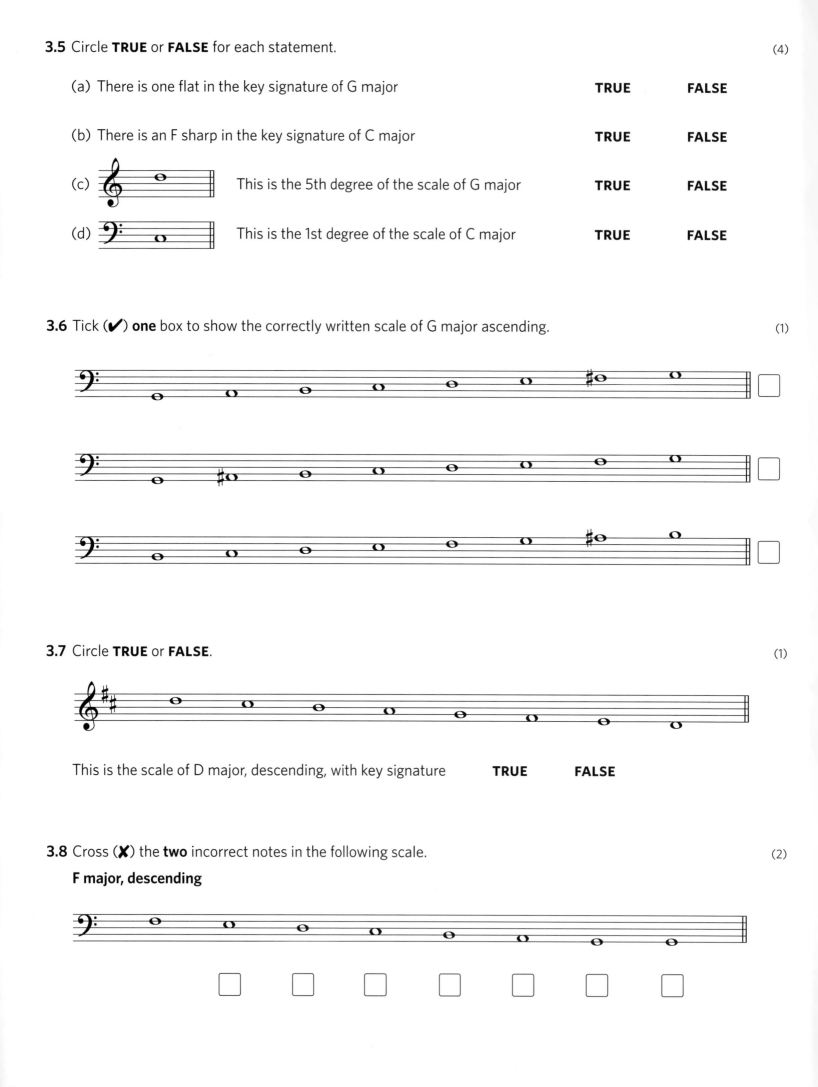

3.7 Circle **TRUE** or **FALSE**. (1)

This is the scale of D major, descending, with key signature   **TRUE**   **FALSE**

3.8 Cross (✗) the **two** incorrect notes in the following scale. (2)

F major, descending

4 Intervals

4.1 For each example, write one note to form the named interval.
Your note should be **higher** than the given note. The key is D major.

(5)

(a)

4th

(b)

8th/8ve

(c)

6th

(d)

2nd

(e)

5th

4.2 Tick (✔) **one** box to show the correct number of each interval. The key is G major.

(5)

(a)

| 5th | 6th | 7th | 8th/8ve |
| □ | □ | □ | □ |

(b)

| 5th | 6th | 7th | 8th/8ve |
| □ | □ | □ | □ |

(c)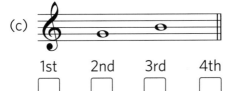

| 1st | 2nd | 3rd | 4th |
| □ | □ | □ | □ |

(d)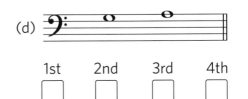

| 1st | 2nd | 3rd | 4th |
| □ | □ | □ | □ |

(e)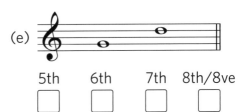

| 5th | 6th | 7th | 8th/8ve |
| □ | □ | □ | □ |

5 Tonic Triads

5.1 Circle **TRUE** or **FALSE** for each statement.

(3)

(a) 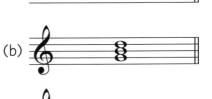   This is the tonic triad of C major   **TRUE**   **FALSE**

(b)   This is the tonic triad of D major   **TRUE**   **FALSE**

(c)   This is the tonic triad of F major   **TRUE**   **FALSE**

5.2 Add **one** missing note to complete each triad, with the tonic as the lowest note. (3)
Use accidentals if necessary.

(a) F major

(b) C major

(c) D major

5.3 Circle the correct key for each tonic triad. (4)

(a) C major   G major   D major   F major

(b) G major   C major   F major   D major

(c) F major   D major   C major   G major

(d) D major   G major   F major   C major

6 Terms and Signs   /5

Tick (✔) **one** box for each term/sign. (5)

diminuendo means:

gradually getting louder ☐

gradually getting quieter ☐

gradually getting slower ☐

gradually getting quicker ☐

pp means:

quiet ☐

moderately quiet ☐

very quiet ☐

very loud ☐

Allegro means:

in a singing style ☐

quick ☐

slow ☐

at a medium speed ☐

♩ ♪ means:

legato: smoothly ☐

legato: detached ☐

staccato: smoothly ☐

staccato: detached ☐

rallentando means:

gradually getting slower ☐

gradually getting louder ☐

slow ☐

gradually getting quicker ☐

Look at this melody and then answer the questions that follow.

7.1 Circle **TRUE** or **FALSE**. (1)

The melody gets gradually louder near the beginning   **TRUE**   **FALSE**

7.2 Tick (✔) the bar number that contains all the notes of the tonic triad of D major. (1)

bar 3 ☐   bar 5 ☐   bar 6 ☐   bar 7 ☐

7.3 Complete the following **three** sentences by ticking one box for each. (3)

(a) The **shortest** note in the melody is a …

dotted crotchet ☐   semiquaver ☐   quaver ☐   minim ☐

(b) Bar 2 has the same pitches as …

bar 3 ☐   bar 4 ☐   bar 5 ☐   bar 6 ☐

(c) The letter name of the **lowest** note in the melody is …

C♯ ☐   F♯ ☐   E ☐   A ☐

Music Theory Sample Papers

ABRSM's official Music Theory Sample Papers are essential resources for candidates preparing for our Music Theory exams. They provide authentic practice material and are a reliable guide as to what to expect in the exam.

- Essential practice material for the new format ABRSM Grade 1 Theory exams
- Model answers also available

Support material for ABRSM Music Theory exams

Supporting the teaching and learning of music in partnership with four Royal Schools of Music

Royal Academy of Music | Royal College of Music
Royal Northern College of Music | Royal Conservatoire of Scotland

www.abrsm.org   f facebook.com/abrsm
𝕏 @abrsm   ▶ ABRSM YouTube

ISBN 978-1-78601-355-2

9 781786 013552

ABRSM